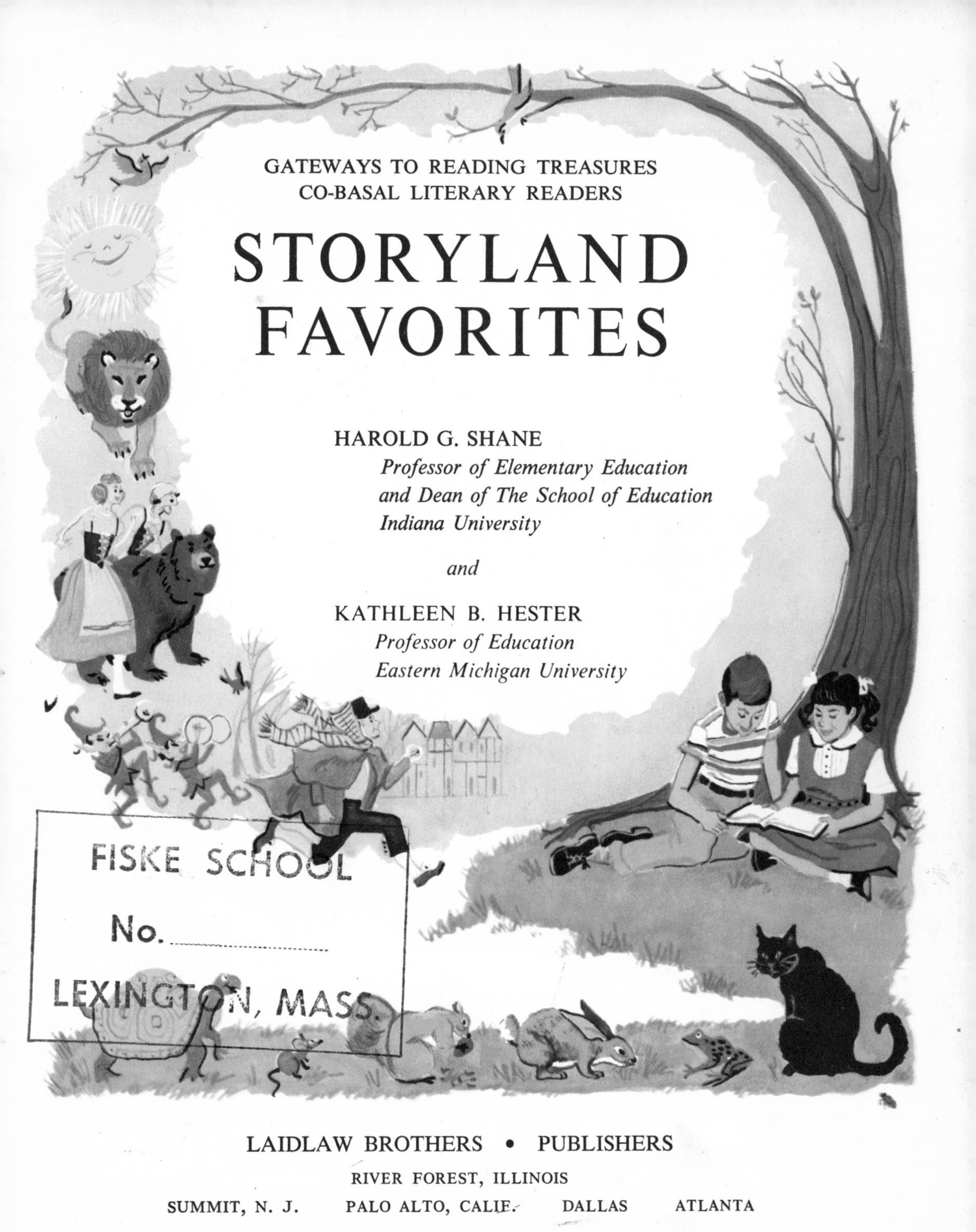

GATEWAYS TO READING TREASURES
CO-BASAL LITERARY READERS

STORYLAND FAVORITES

HAROLD G. SHANE
Professor of Elementary Education
and Dean of The School of Education
Indiana University

and

KATHLEEN B. HESTER
Professor of Education
Eastern Michigan University

LAIDLAW BROTHERS • PUBLISHERS
RIVER FOREST, ILLINOIS
SUMMIT, N. J. PALO ALTO, CALIF. DALLAS ATLANTA

GATEWAYS TO READING TREASURES
CO-BASAL LITERARY READERS

A series of seven readers beginning with the Primer *Tales to Read* followed by a book for each grade one through six.

Tales to Read

Stories to Remember

Storyland Favorites

Doorways to Adventure

Magic and Laughter

Words with Wings

Courage and Adventure

Illustrated by

MARY MILLER SALEM

PRINTED IN THE UNITED STATES OF AMERICA
2 3 4 5 6 7 8 9 6 5 4 3 2 1 0 9

STORIES and POEMS in this BOOK

To Any Reader

As from your house your mother sees
You playing round the garden trees,
So you may see, if you will look
Through the windows of this book,
Another child, far, far away,
And in another garden, play.

Robert Louis Stevenson

The Lion and the Mouse

Have you heard the story of the Lion and the Mouse? It is a very good story.

One day a big lion was sleeping under a tree. He looked very beautiful there in the sun.

A little mouse began to play near the sleeping lion. Soon another mouse began to play near the lion, too.

"Look at me!" said the first mouse. "I am not afraid of this big old lion!" And he ran right over the lion's head.

The other mouse wanted to show his friend that he was not afraid of the sleeping lion. "Just look at what I can do!" he said.

Then, to show that he was not afraid, he ran right up to the lion's head! He stopped near the lion's mouth.

The lion's sleep was about over. He heard the little mouse and he opened one of his eyes. The mouse was so afraid that he could not run.

Then the lion opened his other eye. "Well!" he said, "what are you doing here, little mouse?"

The poor mouse had never been so afraid. He did not know what to say.

"You bad little mouse. I think I will eat you," said the lion.

"Oh, please do not eat me!" said the mouse. "If you will let me go I will help you some day."

The lion thought this was very funny. "How could a little mouse help me?" he asked.

But, because he was not hungry, the lion let the mouse run away.

"Oh, thank you! Thank you very much!" said the mouse. "And I will help you some time when I can."

One day three men came to the woods. They were going to catch the lion.

Can you tell from the picture how the men thought they could catch him?

The next day the lion was out in the warm summer sun. He did not know that there was a big surprise for him when he went around the trees.

He did not know what the three men had done so that they could catch him.

Then, just like that, the lion was caught. He was caught and he could not get out.

He tried and tried to get out. And what a noise he made!

At last the poor lion saw that he could never get out.

The mouse heard the noise that the lion made. He ran to see if he could help the big animal.

When he saw that the lion was caught, the mouse ran up the tree. He saw a way to help the lion who had let him go!

"Mr. Lion," he said, "you let me go a day or two ago. Now I will help you."

"No," said the lion. "Don't take time to help me. The men who caught me will be here soon. I do not want them to get you, too, little friend."

But the good mouse would not go. He began to work to get the lion out.

Then the lion heard the three men coming. "You can't help me now, little friend," he said. "Run and hide in the woods."

"No! No!" said the mouse. "I will have you out in a minute. I can do it!"

And he did! The lion crawled out just in time.

"Ride on my back," the lion said to the mouse, "and I will run into the woods with you."

When the lion and the mouse had run far from the three men, the big animal said, "Thank you, little mouse!"

Then he sang out, "Little friends are good friends. Never again will I say that a mouse is too little to help a lion."

And the lion and the mouse were good friends from that day to this!

The Elves and the Shoemaker

Once there was a shoemaker. His name was Mr. Hans. He lived in a beautiful little house with Mrs. Hans.

Mr. Hans worked from morning to night every day to make shoes. But every day he was poorer and poorer.

At last he had just one little piece of leather from which to cut shoes.

Hans cut out his last shoes. He was not happy. "Dear me," he thought. "We are so poor now! I do not know how we can buy food in a day or two. Soon we will have no food to eat."

It was night-time when Hans had cut out the shoes. "I will make the shoes tomorrow," he said. Then he went to bed.

In the morning Hans had a big surprise. The shoes he had cut out the night before were made! And they were beautiful.

"Come here, my dear," he called to Mrs. Hans. "My shoes are done as if by magic. Come see them!"

Soon a man came to the shoemaker's little house. When he saw the fine new shoes he asked if he could buy them.

After he had gone Hans could buy leather for four new shoes. And Mrs. Hans could go to the store to get food for them to eat.

That night the shoemaker cut four shoes from his new piece of leather. When he got out of bed in the morning, the four shoes were all ready for someone to buy. They were as well made and as pretty as the shoes had been the day before.

Soon everyone came to buy the beautiful shoes. And Hans and Mrs. Hans were very happy.

Day after day Hans would buy more leather and cut out more shoes.

Night after night the fine new shoes would be made.

Men came from far away to look at the shoes and to buy them. Soon Hans and Mrs. Hans had all the food they could eat.

But not once did Hans or Mrs. Hans see who made the shoes.

One night Hans and Mrs. Hans sat near their fire. It was a cold night. They could hear the wind and see the snow through the window.

"Soon it will be Christmas," the good woman said. "I wish we knew what friend has helped us. Then we could do something for him."

"We can hide here," said Hans. "If we do we can see who our friend is."

And that is what the good man and the good woman did.

Soon Hans and his wife heard a little noise. They saw the door fly open! In came two little men. They were elves!

The elves were at work in a minute. And how fast they did go! In no time at all the shoes were made and ready for the next day.

When the work was done, the elves opened the door and went away over the cold, white snow.

"Oh, the poor little elves!" said Mrs. Hans. "Did you see their feet? They have no shoes, and they had so little on that they were blue with cold!"

"Hans," the good woman said, "we must make some shoes and coats for our friends before Christmas." And so they did.

It was very near Christmas. Hans and Mrs. Hans worked all day long for five days. Mrs. Hans made two warm red coats. And Hans made warm little green shoes that were just right for the elves' feet.

On the night before Christmas the big surprise was ready for the elves.

Hans put the red coats and leather shoes near the door. After that he and Mrs. Hans just had time to hide.

In the door came two elves. They were cold and had no shoes. Then they saw the beautiful coats and the new shoes. "Look!" said one. "They are for us. They are ours!" And the elves put them on.

What fun they had! They jumped about and sang to show how warm and happy they were. Then they went out and shut the door.

Hans never saw the elves again. But he and his good woman were always happy and had all the food they could eat.

Every Christmas night Mrs. Hans put a little cake near the door. Every Christmas morning the cake was gone. And Mr. and Mrs. Hans could see where the little shoes had come over the snow.

The Little Shoemakers

Here is the way we make our shoes,
We make our shoes,
We make our shoes,

Here is the way we make our shoes
So pretty
In the night.

How the Bear Lost His Tail

In the days of old the bear had a long, beautiful tail. This is the story of how he lost it.

It was a very cold day. The first snow was all around. You could not see the plants in the gardens.

A bear was out in the snow. He wanted to find something more to eat before he began his long sleep.

Soon the bear met a bad red fox. The fox had some fish.

"Good day, Mr. Fox," said the bear. "Where did you get the fine fish?"

"I got them from the river," said Mr. Fox.

"They are beautiful fish!" said the bear. "Can you show me how to get some?"

"I will be happy to help you, Mr. Bear," the fox said. "After I hide my fish in this old tree we will go to the river. I will show you how to get some fish."

The fox and the bear went over the cold snow to the river. When they got there, the bad fox told the bear what to do to get some fish.

"First," said the fox, "you must go out on the ice and cut a hole. Then you must stick your tail through the hole and into the water."

The bear did just what the fox told him to do.

He cut a hole in the ice and sat down near it with his tail in the water.

"Now what do I do?" asked the bear.

"You must stay there for a long, long time," the fox told him. "The longer you stay the more fish you will catch."

The bear sat on the ice for a long time after the fox had gone away.

Soon the bear was very cold. But he did not get up. He wanted to get all the fish he could catch.

After a time the sun began to go down. "I must have many fish by now," said the bear. At last he tried to get up.

But something had caught his beautiful tail!

Poor Mr. Bear could not get his tail out of the hole. His tail was caught in the ice!

He tried and tried to get away, but he could not. At last he tried to jump to get out of the ice. He made a big jump. Off came his tail!

And that is why the bear has gone about with a little tail to this very day.

The Three Wishes

There was once a poor farmer named Paddy. He lived in an old house with his brother.

The two brothers were not happy. They wanted a fine house and a big farm. They wanted many horses and cows.

One day Paddy and his brother John were at work in their little garden. They heard someone call them. "Who can it be?" asked John.

In a minute Paddy said, "I heard someone cry out again!"

"Yes," said John. "I heard him, too. I think he is near the trees."

The two brothers ran to see who had called them. Soon they were surprised to find a little old man who was caught under a tree. Because he was so little John and Paddy knew him. They knew that the old man was one of the elves who lived nearby.

"Well," said the little man. "Don't just look at me! Help me get out from under this tree!"

"We will help you," said John.

"Oh, no!" said Paddy. "Let us ask for something first."

"We are very poor, Mr. Elf. Will you give us three wishes if we let you go?" asked Paddy.

The little man did not want to give the brothers three wishes. "Very well," said Paddy. "Then you can stay under that tree all summer!"

At last the elf told the brothers that they could have the three wishes. Then Paddy and John helped him as he crawled out from under the tree.

"I said you could have three wishes," the elf told the brothers. "You can have them. But they will not make you happy." Then, as if by magic, he was gone.

Paddy and John went back to their little old house. They sat down near the fire. "What should we wish for?" asked John.

"I think that I am going to wish for a big farm," said Paddy.

"And I guess that I will wish for a fine house," said John.

"Then for the last wish we can ask for many horses and cows," Paddy told his brother.

"Let us eat dinner before we make our wishes," said John.

"All right," said Paddy. "But I wish we had a pot of soup ready. Then we could make our wishes now."

Paddy had no sooner made this wish than there was a pot of soup on the hot fire!

"Oh, dear," said John. "Look what you have done! You have lost one of our wishes for us."

Then, before John had time to think of what he was doing, he said, "I wish that pot of soup were on your nose!"

And just like that the pot of soup was on Paddy's nose.

"Now see what you have done," said Paddy. "You have made another wish! Now help me get this pot off."

But nothing they did helped. The brothers could not get the pot off Paddy's nose.

After a while John said, "Well, we have not used our last wish. I can ask for a big farm, or the fine house, or the horses and cows."

"What!" said Paddy. "And let me go around with this pot of soup on my nose? Never!"

"But, Paddy, if we don't wish for the farm, or the house, or the farm animals, we will never get them. Don't you think you could live with the pot of soup on your nose?"

"Oh, no, I can't do that. We must wish the pot of soup off my nose, John."

At last John said that he would wish the pot off Paddy's nose. He did so and the pot was gone. And so was the last of the wishes.

The elf had been right. John and Paddy had three wishes that they made the little old man give them. But the brothers were not happy. And they were just as poor as they had been before.

The Rabbit and the Turtle

Once there was a rabbit who could run very fast. But no one liked the rabbit because he always told his friends how good he was.

"I can run faster than you can," he would say to all his animal friends.

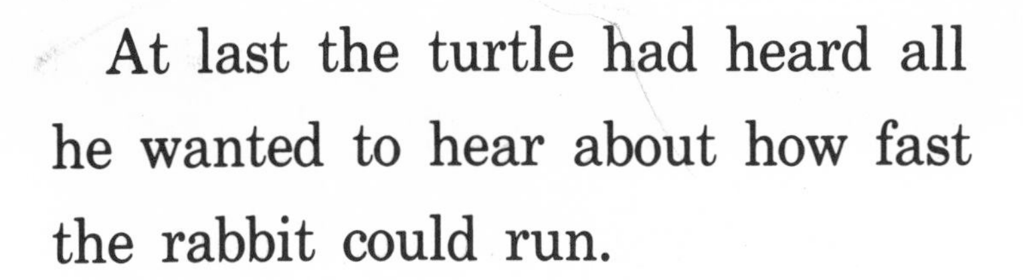

At last the turtle had heard all he wanted to hear about how fast the rabbit could run.

"You are not so good, Mr. Rabbit," said the turtle. "Why, I can run as fast as you can!"

"You funny old turtle!" said the rabbit. "I could run from here to the big tree before you could crawl to the road."

"Very well, Mr. Rabbit," said the turtle. "Let us see who can get to the big tree first."

"I am ready to go now," said the rabbit and he began to run.

The turtle crawled after him.

It was a warm day. By the time he came to the road the rabbit wanted to go to sleep.

The turtle was so far away that the rabbit could not see him. "I have time to sleep here in the sun!" the rabbit said. So he stopped running, shut his eyes, and went to sleep.

The old turtle never stopped. He crawled on and on. He came to the road and crawled on under the hot sun.

The turtle wanted to go to sleep, too. It was work for him to go so far, but on he went.

At last the rabbit opened his eyes. He looked across the road. Then, far away, he saw the turtle crawling on his way to the big tree.

The rabbit jumped up in surprise. Then he began to run just as fast as he could go. He ran and ran so that he could get to the big tree before the turtle got there.

But the turtle crawled to the big tree first! The rabbit could not catch up with him.

Never again did the rabbit tell his animal friends how fast he could run. He knew that they would tell him that he could not run as fast as a turtle.

The Fox and the Crow

A crow sat in a tree near a little house. He looked in the open window. He saw some good things to eat.

The crow went to the window. He looked around. There was no one near. He went in and quickly took some food.

The crow went flying out of the window. He had food in his mouth.

He went to the top of an old tree in the woods.

A hungry fox saw the crow fly to the old tree. He wanted the food that the big black bird had taken.

The fox went over to the tree. "Good morning, Mr. Crow," he said. "You are a very beautiful bird."

This made the crow very happy. He liked to hear that he was beautiful.

"You are so very pretty!" said the fox. "I would like it if you sang something for me. I am sure you will be beautiful to hear."

The crow was pleased. He liked the good things the fox had said.

"Please, let me hear you sing," the fox asked again.

The poor crow opened his mouth and down fell the food!

"Oh, dear!" said the old crow. "Oh, dear me. I have lost my food!"

The hungry fox ate the food quickly. Then he said, "You funny-looking old bird! After this you will think before you open your mouth!"

The Boy and the North Wind

A boy once lived with his mother in a little old house. The house was on a farm. On the farm there was a cow.

The farm gave the boy and his mother a little food to eat. The cow gave them some milk.

On many cold days the boy and his mother had very little food. They were always hungry. For their dinner they had some gingerbread and milk.

The North Wind came to their little home. He made the window fly open. The milk fell over and ran under the boy's feet.

"The North Wind can not do this to us," said the boy. "He must give us more milk."

"Yes, Jack," his mother said. "Run after the North Wind. Tell him that he must give us something for the milk."

Jack put on his hat and coat. He ran out of the house. He could see the North Wind. The North Wind was far away across the snow.

"Come back!" Jack called. But the North Wind ran on. Then Jack ran after the bad North Wind.

He ran and ran. He ran through the woods and down an old road. He ran across farms that were white with new snow.

The North Wind went quickly from town to town. He went through the city and across white hills. And Jack came right after him.

At last the Wind went to his home. Jack went up to the door. The North Wind let him in.

The boy said, "You must give us something for the milk we lost."

The North Wind wanted to play. But he was not a bad little man. "Very well," he said. "Take this magic gingerbread. You may cut off as many pieces as you wish. There will always be more of it to eat!"

Then Jack went on his way. By this time it was morning. He stopped at a farm house. He asked if he could eat and sleep there. The farmer told him to come in.

The farmer was not a good man. He was a bad man. He saw Jack cut pieces from his magic gingerbread. He saw that there was always more gingerbread to eat!

When Jack was sleeping the farmer took the magic gingerbread. He gave Jack some gingerbread that was not magic.

Jack went home with the gingerbread. When he got there he found the gingerbread had lost the magic. When he cut off the last piece there was no more to eat!

The boy went back to the home of the North Wind. "You must give me something new," he said. "The gingerbread is all gone!"

The Wind gave him a magic pot of soup. Jack could take all the soup he wanted from the pot. There was always more in it!

Jack again stopped at the farm to eat and sleep. The bad farmer saw that Jack had a magic soup pot.

When Jack was sleeping, the man put another pot near Jack and took the magic one.

After the boy went home he found the pot had lost the magic. When the soup was gone there was no more.

Once again Jack went to the home of the North Wind.

"This is the last time I will help you," said the North Wind.

"Take this magic stick," the Wind told Jack. "It will help you if you say 'Work, stick, work!' "

"Thank you. Thank you very much," said Jack. Then he began to make his way home.

Once more Jack stopped at the farm house. The farmer was pleased to see him. He asked Jack to come in to eat and sleep.

The bad farmer saw Jack's stick. He was sure that it was a magic stick. When Jack was sleeping, the farmer took the stick.

Just then Jack opened his eyes. "Work, stick, work!" he called out. And the stick began to go after the farmer.

Again and again it came down on the bad man. "Help! Help!" cried the farmer. "Stop your stick and I will give back your magic gingerbread. I will give back the magic pot."

"Stop, stick, stop!" said Jack, and the stick jumped back to the boy.

"Now give me my magic gingerbread. Give me my magic pot," said Jack. "Or I will tell the stick to go after you again!"

The farmer quickly gave up the gingerbread. He gave up the magic pot.

Jack went home. And every day after that Jack and his mother had all they wanted to eat!

What Are Little Boys Made Of?

What are little boys made of?
What are little boys made of?

and and little
dogs' tails,
That's what little boys are made of.

Gudbrand on the Hill

There once was a man named Gudbrand. He lived in a farm house on a hill. He was called Gudbrand on the Hill.

Mrs. Gudbrand was a very good woman. She thought that there was no better man than Gudbrand. What he did, she always thought was the right thing to do.

One day the good woman said to Gudbrand, "I want you to go to the city. Get some money for our cow so that we can buy food to eat."

Gudbrand went down the hill with the cow. The city was far away.

On the way to the city Gudbrand met a man. The man had a very old horse. He said to Gudbrand, "I will give you my fine horse for your little old cow."

"All right," said Gudbrand, and he gave away his fine cow.

After a while Gudbrand met a little old woman. She had a big brown dog.

"Good day," said the woman.

"Good day," said Gudbrand.

"What a poor old horse you have," she said. "Take my fine dog and I will give your horse a good home and good food to eat."

Gudbrand took the dog and went on his way to the town. Before he got there he met a boy. The boy gave Gudbrand a white kitten for the brown dog.

At last Gudbrand came to the little city. He had come a long way. He was hungry. The kitten was hungry, too.

Then Gudbrand saw a man who had some cakes and milk. "Please let me buy some cake," said Gudbrand. "Let me buy some milk for my little white cat."

The man gave Gudbrand and his kitten the cake and milk.

Gudbrand and the cat liked the cake and milk. When the food was gone the man said to Gudbrand, "Now what will you give me for the cake and milk?"

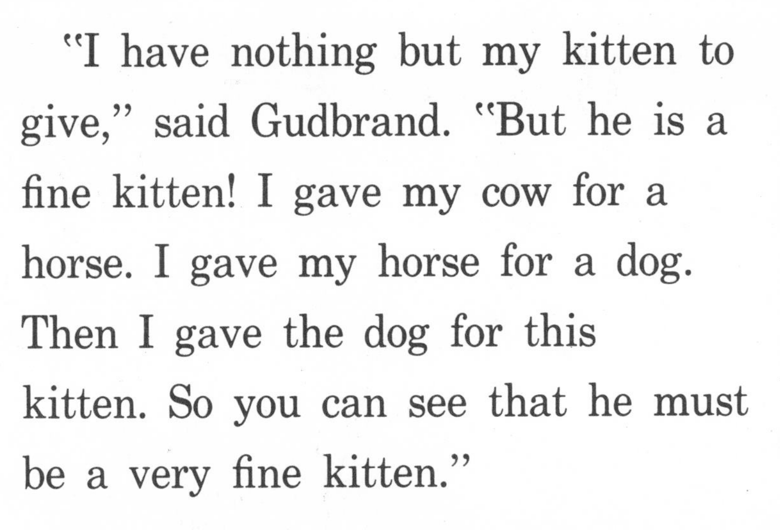

"I have nothing but my kitten to give," said Gudbrand. "But he is a fine kitten! I gave my cow for a horse. I gave my horse for a dog. Then I gave the dog for this kitten. So you can see that he must be a very fine kitten."

The man took Gudbrand's kitten for the cake and milk.

A good man with a bag of gold had heard Gudbrand tell his story. He went up to Gudbrand. "You gave away your cow and now you do not have a thing to take back. Mrs. Gudbrand will not be happy when you get home!"

"Oh, yes she will," said Gudbrand. "I have a good woman. She will be happy when I tell her what I did."

"If Mrs. Gudbrand is happy when you tell her what you got for the cow, I will give you five pieces of gold," the man with the gold said.

"And if she is not happy," said Gudbrand, "I will give you my farm."

Gudbrand took the good man to his home on the side of the hill. When they got there the man said, "I will hide here by the door. Then I can hear what your wife has to say!"

Gudbrand went into the house. Mrs. Gudbrand came to see him. "Did you get the money for our cow?" she asked. "What did you get for her?"

Gudbrand told his story so that the good man with the bag of gold could hear him. "Well, my dear," he said, "I gave the cow to a man for his horse."

"That is good," said Mrs. Gudbrand. "Now we will have a horse to ride."

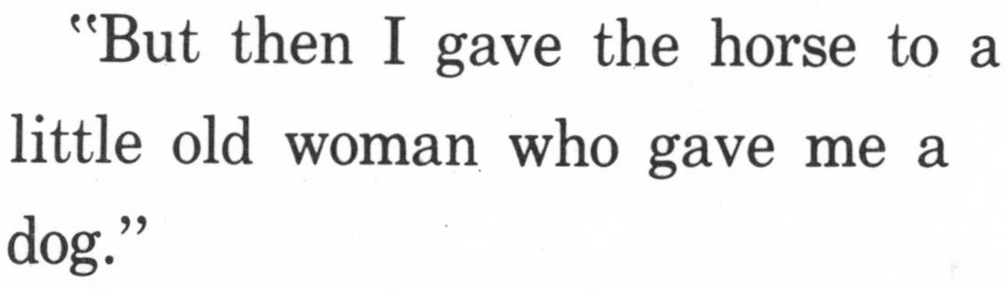

"But then I gave the horse to a little old woman who gave me a dog."

"That is better," said Mrs. Gudbrand. "I have wanted a dog for a long time."

"But then I gave the dog to a little boy. He gave me a white kitten for the dog."

"So much the better," the good woman said. "I like cats, and we do not have one."

"But when I got to town I was hungry," said Gudbrand. "I gave the kitten to a man for some cake and milk."

"You did just the right thing," said Mrs. Gudbrand. "I would not want you to go hungry. Now come and sit down to dinner."

The good man with the bag of gold heard all he wanted to hear. He came in the door. "You have the best woman I know of," he told Gudbrand. "Here are your five pieces of gold!"

And that is how Gudbrand on the Hill gave away his cow for milk and cake but got five pieces of gold.

The Cat and the Milk

There was once an old woman who had a black cat.

One day the old woman milked her cow.

"Now I must go to town," she said. "Where can I put this milk so the cat will not get it?

"I know! I will put it in this jug! It is so little that my cat can not crawl into it!"

After the old woman had gone to town the cat said, "Now how can I get that milk?"

The cat tried and tried. But he could not crawl into the jug to get some milk.

After a while he sat down to think. At last he said, "I have it! I know how I can get that milk!"

The cat ran out of the house. He came back with some stones. He put the stones into the jug. Each time he put in a stone the milk came nearer the top of the jug.

After a while the milk came right to the top of the jug. The cat could have all the milk he wanted!

When the little old woman came home she saw what the cat had done.

"Well!" said she, "this is the last time I let you into the house. After this you will go to town with me!"

My

I have a little [shadow] that goes
in and out with me,
And what can be the use of him is
more than I can see.
He is very, very like me from
[heels] up to the head;
And I see him jump before me, when
I jump into my bed.

The Bear, the Man, and the Fox

One day a big black bear was caught in a trap. He tried and tried to get out.

At last he cried for help. "Please, please!" he called. "Will someone get me out of here?"

A man heard the bear calling. He ran to see why the bear was crying for help.

When the bear saw the man he said, "Dear friend, let me out."

"Oh, no!" said the man. "If I let you out you will eat me."

"It is not so!" said the black bear. "I will be your friend. I will give you anything you want. Just please let me out."

At last the good man gave in. He opened the door to the trap.

Out jumped the bear. He caught the man. "Now I will eat you up!" he said. "I was in the trap a long time. I am very hungry."

"Stop!" said the man. "Let us ask the first three things we see if it is all right for you to eat me."

"Very well," said the bear. "You may ask the first three things that we see. I am sure they will say that I may eat you up."

The first thing they met was a tree. "Why, sure, the bear may eat you," the tree said. "I am good to men and what do they do to me and my brothers? They cut us up and put us in their fires!

"Be a man! Let the bear eat you!"

Just then a duck came flying by. "Stop! Please come here, little duck," the man asked.

"What do you want?" asked the duck. The man told the duck the story.

"Well," said the duck, "I think the bear may eat you up! You men eat us when you catch us. I would like to see the bear eat you."

After the duck had gone away the bear and the man met a fox.

"Dear friend fox," said the man, "we want you to hear our story."

He began to tell how he had let the big animal out of the trap. He made the story just as long as he could.

"Oh dear," said the fox. "Now how did you say this all began? You say you were in the trap and the bear let you out?"

"No! No!" said the bear. "I was in the trap."

"Oh, yes. I see! I was in the trap," said the fox. "No, I was not in the trap. Dear me! Who was in the trap?"

The bear began over again. "I said I was in the trap. The man let me out."

"But how could the man let me out?" asked the fox. "I was not in the trap."

"Now look here," said the bear. "I will show you how it was. I am the bear. This is the trap. I will now go back into the trap."

The big animal went back into the trap. "This is where the man found me," said the bear.

The fox quickly shut the door of the trap.

"Oh," said the fox. "Now I see how it was! You were in the trap, Mr. Bear. The man came by the door. He let you out. Now you are back in the trap!"

"Yes! Yes!" said the bear. "Now let me out again."

"Oh, no!" said the fox. "If I may say so, I think you are just where you had better be!"

Snow-White and Rose-Red

There was once an old woman. She had two beautiful girls. They were called Snow-White and Rose-Red.

The two girls were as good as they could be. They always liked to help their mother. They made the beds and helped to get dinner ready. Snow-White would make the fire each night. Rose-Red would bring water from the well.

One cold night the girls sat by the fire. All at once they heard someone at the door. "See who it is," said Mother to Snow-White.

Snow-White ran to the door. "Who is there?" she asked.

"Please let me in. I am cold," someone said.

"Open the door," said Mother. "It is some poor man who has been out in the snow."

Snow-White opened the door. A big black bear put his head into the room. The girl cried out and jumped back!

"Do not be afraid," said the bear. "I just want to get warm by your fire."

"Do come in," said Mother to the bear. "But do not go too near the fire. Your fine coat might catch on fire."

The bear came to the little house every night after that. Snow-White and Rose-Red had fun playing with him.

Every night the bear would sleep near the fire. In the morning he would go away.

At last the snows were over. "Now," said the bear, "I must go away. I will not be back until it snows again."

"Why must you go, dear bear?" asked Snow-White and Rose-Red.

"I hide my gold in the far-away hills," said the bear. "I must keep my eye on it. If I do not, a bad old elf will take it from me. He sleeps all the time it is cold. Now that it is warm he will get up and look for my gold!"

The bear said good-by to the girls. They were not happy to see him go. But they were happy to hear that he would come back when the snow fell again.

Some time after that the mother asked the girls to go to town. She told them to buy new coats and shoes. "And buy some milk, too," she said.

The road to town went across a river. It went through a woods where there were big trees. It took the girls by pretty farms where flowers were growing in the little gardens.

On their way home the girls heard someone calling for help. They ran around the big trees.

Soon they came to an opening in the woods. There they found a little old man. It was the elf who lived in the woods.

A big bird had caught the elf. It tried to fly away with him. Rose-Red found a big stick. She went after the big bird. She tried to make the bird let go of the little man.

At last the big bird gave up. He let the elf go. The girls and the little man saw him fly away over the tree tops.

The elf took off his hat. He thanked the girls for helping him. Then he said, "What can I do for you? I can work magic. Would you like me to give you a new house? Or a puppy? Or a fine, fat cow to give you milk? I will give you what you ask for."

The girls looked at one another. Then Rose-Red asked, "Do you know a big black bear who lives in the woods near here?"

After a minute the little old man said, "Yes, I know the bear."

"Well," said Snow-White, "we want you to stop taking his gold! Then he will not have to look after it all summer long. He can come back to our house to play."

For a long time the little man did not say a thing. Then he said, "Very well. Come with me to the bear's house."

He took the girls through the woods. He took them up the side of a hill on which the bear lived. At last they came to a hole in the hill.

"Come out, Mr. Bear, come out," the little old man called.

When the bear came out the old man said, "I am going to tell the girls a story.

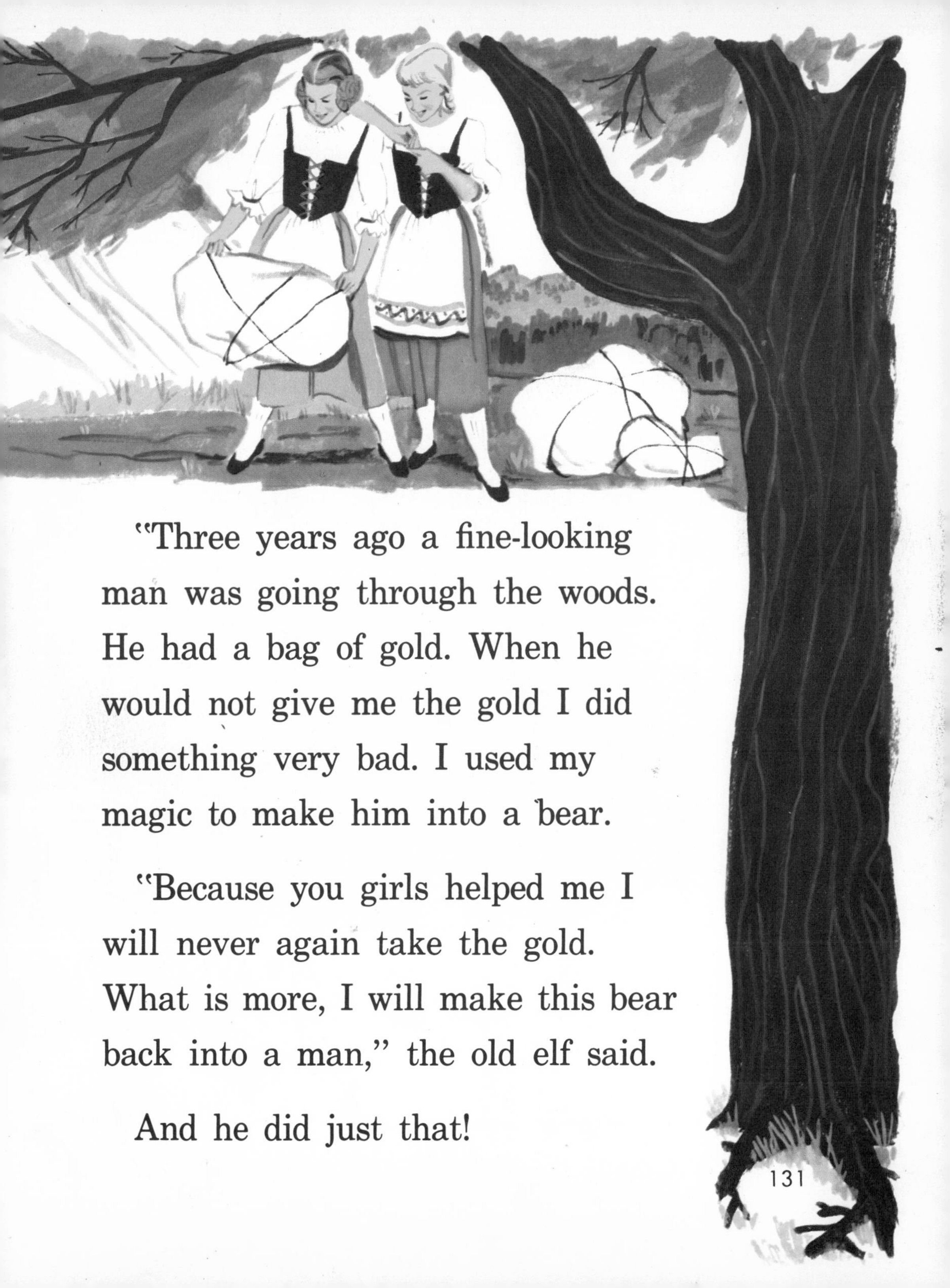

"Three years ago a fine-looking man was going through the woods. He had a bag of gold. When he would not give me the gold I did something very bad. I used my magic to make him into a bear.

"Because you girls helped me I will never again take the gold. What is more, I will make this bear back into a man," the old elf said.

And he did just that!

When the bear had been made back into a man the first thing he said was, "Thank you, Rose-Red! Thank you, Snow-White!

"Because you are good as well as beautiful you have helped this little old man. You have helped me.

"Now I am going to give each of you some of my gold. I know you will use it well."

Snow-White and Rose-Red said good-by and ran home. They lived for many years. They were always happy and they were always good to others.

Rain Fairies

Rain fairies playing on my garden
bed,
Each little flower puts up its head.

Sun fairies laugh and see the
flowers play.
Now, little rain fairies, you must
fly away.

Fly to your cloud home, far up in
the .
Come, little sun fairies; rain
fairies, good-by.

The Wind and the Sun

One fine day the Wind met the Sun.

"I am better than you are," said the Wind to the Sun.

"Oh, no," said the Sun. "I am the better of the two."

Soon they saw a man coming down the road. The Sun said, "I know how we can tell who is the better. Let us see who can make that man take off his coat. If one of us can make him take it off he is the better."

"All right, Mr. Sun," said the Wind. "You go in back of a cloud. I will show you how quickly I can get the man out of his coat!"

The Wind made a big noise. He tried to get the man out of his coat. He tried and tried! But all the man did was to draw his coat more closely around him.

At last the Wind gave up. "Come out of the cloud, Mr. Sun," he said. "I for one can not get this man to take off his coat."

The Sun now began to come through the clouds. He made everything very warm. Soon the man on the road opened his coat.

Then the Sun began to get hot. In two minutes the man took off his coat.

"You see," said the Sun, "if one is good he will not have to make a big noise. You do not have to go around telling everyone how good you are."

For Every Day

Father, we thank You for the night,
And for the pretty morning light;
For tales to read and friends for play,
And all that makes a happy day.

Help us to do the things we should,
To be to others kind and good;
In all we do in work or play,
To grow better in every way.